SMARTEST PET

FASTEST PET

SNUGGLIEST PET

NAUGHTIEST PET

SHAGGIEST PET

This igloo book belongs to...

....

....

....

CLUMSIEST PET

GRIZZLIEST PET

SNOBBIEST PET

FUNNIEST PET

GUILTIEST PET

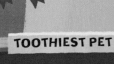

TOOTHIEST PET

CLUCKIEST PET

FOXIEST PET

HOPPIEST PET

CERTIFICATE OF
AWESOMENESS

Published in 2017
by Igloo Books Ltd
Cottage Farm
Sywell
NN6 0BJ
www.igloobooks.com

LEO002 0217
2 4 6 8 10 9 7 5 3 1
ISBN 978-1-78670-596-9

Illustrated by Bob Kolar
Original story by Molly Wigand

Cover designed by Nicholas Gage
Interiors designed by Richard Sykes
Edited by Hannah Cather

Printed and manufactured in China

THE MOST
AWESOME
PET
IN THE WORLD

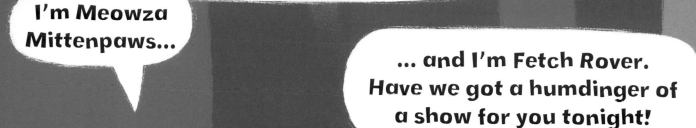

EXTINCTEST PET

LONGEST PET

INVISIBLEST PET

OUCHIEST PET

It's almost time to reveal **THE MOST AWESOME PET IN THE WORLD.** But first, a very special look at the **Pet Hall of Fame.**

LONGEST PET (cont'd)
SPACIEST PET
DUMBEST PET
Well, that was fascinating. Now, back to the show.
MOST SHOCKING PET